INFOGRAPHICS FOR KIDS

ACTIVITY BOOK

RESEARCHED AND WRITTEN BY
SUSAN MARTINEAU

DESIGNED AND ILLUSTRATED BY
VICKY BARKER

www.bsmall.co.uk

Published by b small publishing ltd. www.bsmall.co.uk © b small publishing ltd. 2014 • 1 2 3 4 5 • ISBN 978-1-909767-57-7 •
Production by Madeleine Ehm. Printed in China by WKT Co. Ltd.

WHAT IS AN INFOGRAPHIC?

Infographics show us information using **PICTURES** as well as **WORDS** and **NUMBERS.**
Our brains are really good at making sense of pictures. It takes our brains longer to work out what words are trying to tell us. This means that pictures can be really helpful when we are trying to understand something.

INFOGRAPHIC IS SHORT FOR 'INFORMATION GRAPHIC'.

INFORMATION = FACTS AND NUMBERS OR EVEN A STORY.

GRAPHIC = AN ILLUSTRATION OR PICTURE.

INFOGRAPHICS ARE USED TO:

COMPARE different facts or sets of numbers.

EXPLAIN how something works.

SHOW how things are connected.

LIST facts and numbers.

When we are looking at infographics we need to look carefully at the way they use different

LETTER AND NUMBER SIZES

OUTLINES

COLOURS

SHAPES

ARROWS AND BOXES

Infographics help us to 'picture' what numbers are trying to tell us and to visualise what they really mean.

= 1 LITRE

= 3 LITRES

INFOGRAPHICS MAKE IT EASIER FOR US TO → **UNDERSTAND INFORMATION** → **LEARN IT AND REMEMBER IT!**

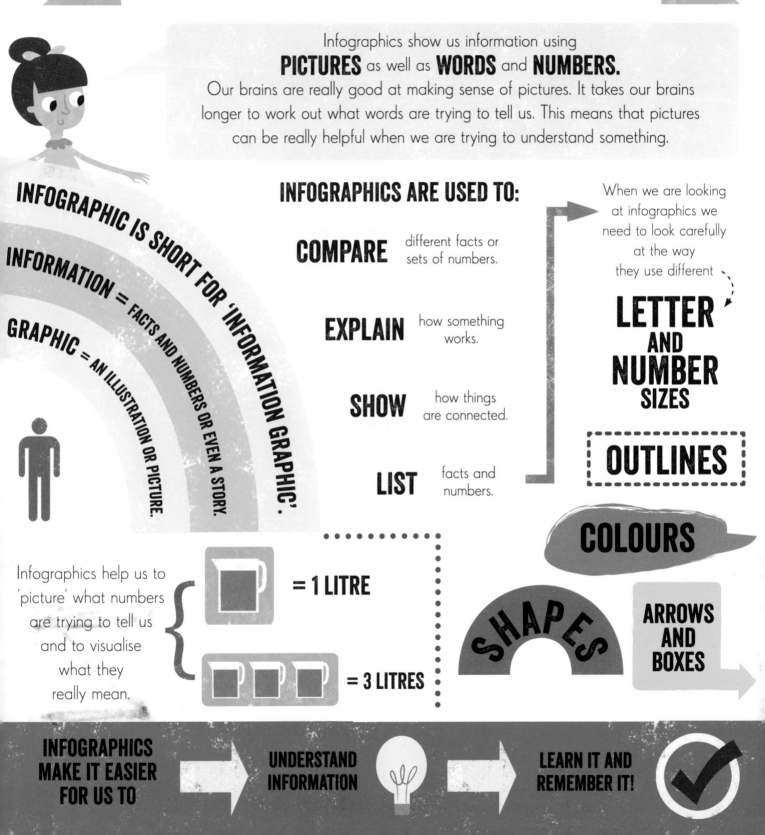

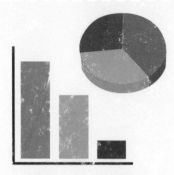

CHARTS, GRAPHS AND PIE CHARTS

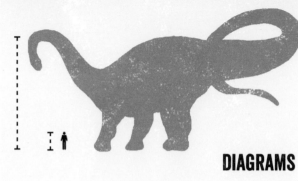

DIAGRAMS

1860s
Penny-farthing

1865
Boneshaker

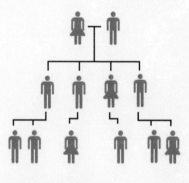

1885
Safety bicycle

TIMELINES

INFOGRAPHICS
COME IN ALL SHAPES AND STYLES

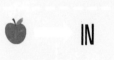 **IN**

MOUTH

STOMACH

SMALL INTESTINE

LARGE INTESTINE

 **OUT**

FLOW CHARTS

MAPS AND PLANS

POEMS
KNOWLEDGE
BOOKS
COMICS STORIES

WORD CLOUDS

FAMILY TREES

MANY OF THE INFOGRAPHICS IN THIS BOOK ALSO INCLUDE AN ACTIVITY FOR YOU TO DO.

LOOK FOR THE FOLLOWING SYMBOLS:

DRAW OR WRITE IN THE BOOK.

DO YOUR OWN RESEARCH FOR MORE INFORMATION.

STANDING UP
TO THE DINOSAURS

Imagine we could go back in time.
This is how we would have looked standing next to the dinosaurs.

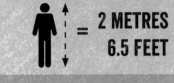 = **2 METRES**
6.5 FEET

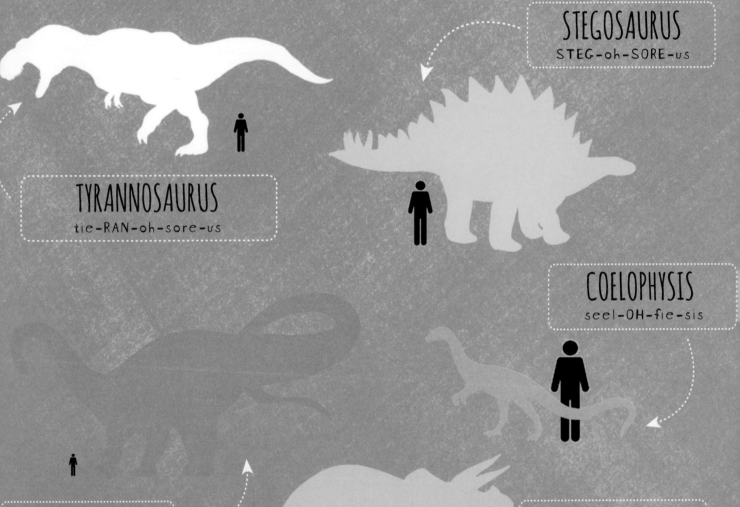

STEGOSAURUS
STEG-oh-SORE-us

TYRANNOSAURUS
tie-RAN-oh-sore-us

COELOPHYSIS
seel-OH-fie-sis

DIPLODOCUS
DIP-low-DOCK-us

TRICERATOPS
tri-SERRA-tops

COLOUR IN THE DINOSAURS.

GROWING BABIES

HUMAN BABIES take **NINE MONTHS** to grow inside their mothers.

Have a look at how long it takes for other baby creatures to be ready to be born.

RABBIT
28-31 DAYS
(1 MONTH)

MOUSE
19-21 DAYS

DOG
2 MONTHS
(9 WEEKS)

KANGAROO
30-36 DAYS

SKYSCRAPERS OF THE RAINFOREST

Tropical rainforests are like amazing high-rise buildings.
A **HUGE** number of creatures and plants live
on different storeys.

EMERGENT LAYER

= the
height of

33 👤 men

CANOPY

=
the height of

20 👤 men

UNDERSTOREY

=
the height of

10 👤 men

FOREST FLOOR

=
the height of

1 👤 man

COLOUR THESE ANIMALS SO THEY ARE READY TO FIND THEIR FOREST HOME.

CAN YOU FIND OUT MORE ABOUT THESE ANIMALS AND WHERE THEY LIVE.

The trees of a tropical rainforest are so close together that rain falling on the canopy can take as long as 10 minutes to reach the ground.

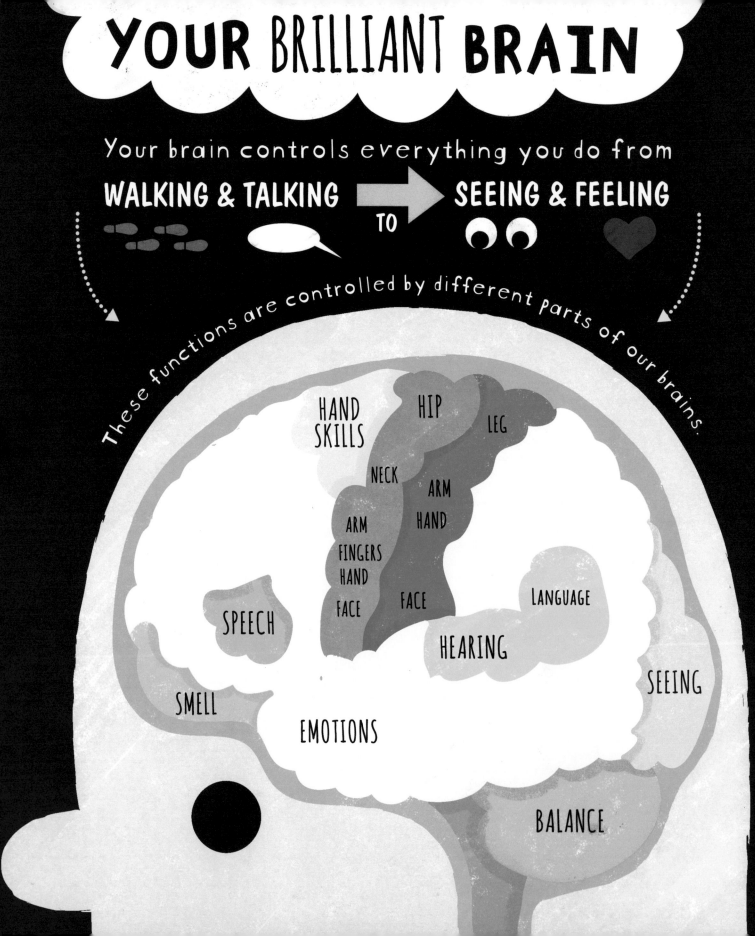

DRAW YOURSELF DANCING AND SINGING. WHICH BITS OF YOUR BRAIN WILL YOU BE USING AS YOU PERFORM?

FOOD FACTORY

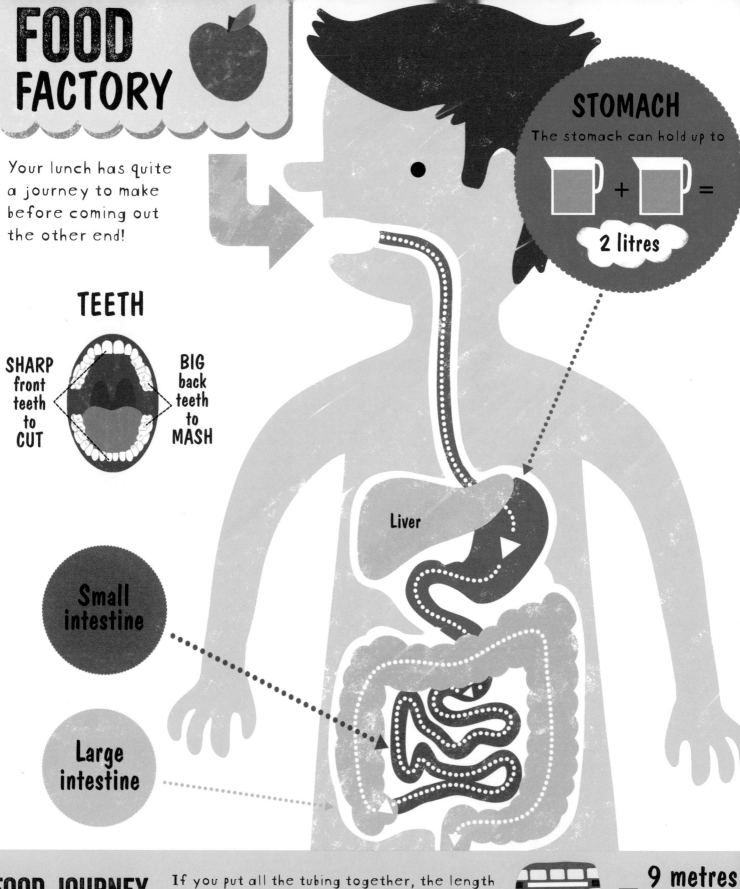

Your lunch has quite a journey to make before coming out the other end!

STOMACH

The stomach can hold up to

+ = 2 litres

TEETH

SHARP front teeth to CUT

BIG back teeth to MASH

Small intestine

Large intestine

Liver

FOOD JOURNEY If you put all the tubing together, the length would be the same as a double-decker bus.

 = **9 metres (29.5 feet)**

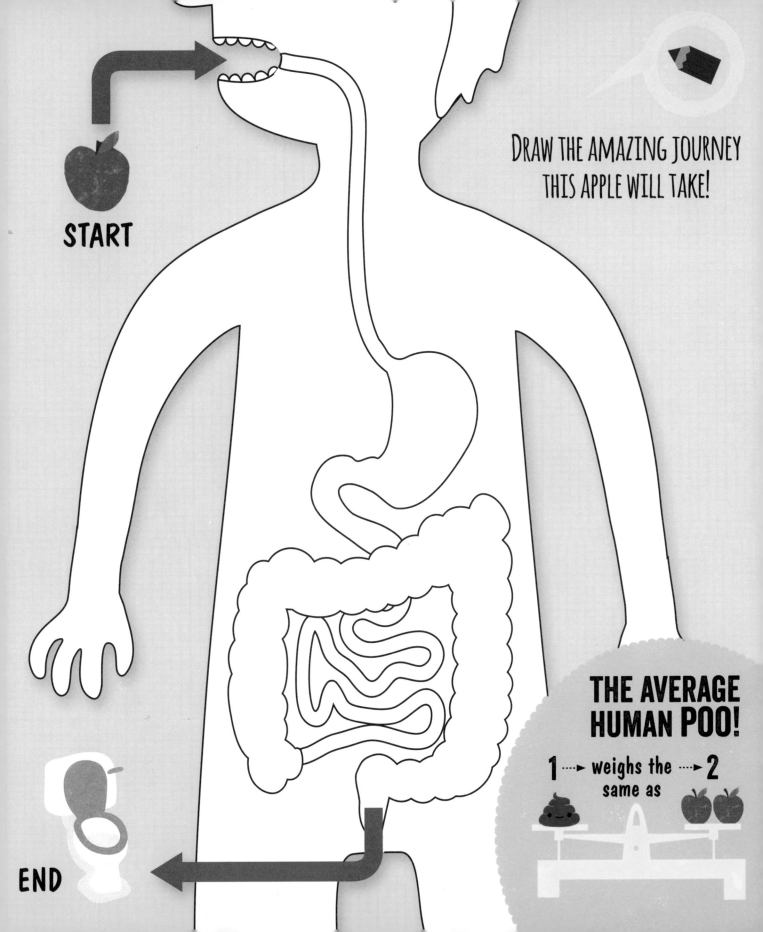

START

DRAW THE AMAZING JOURNEY
THIS APPLE WILL TAKE!

THE AVERAGE
HUMAN POO!

1 ····> weighs the ····> 2
        same as

END

OUR SENSES

Our senses tell us what is going on around us by sending messages to our brains.

HEARING

The ear canal joins the outer ear to the eardrum. It is

3 CM

or 1.18 inches long.

The eardrum is the size of your fingernail.

SIGHT

IF YOU
CAN CLEARLY
SEE LETTERS ON
AN EYE CHART FROM
20 FEET (OR 6 METRES)
AWAY IT MEANS YOU HAVE
PERFECT SIGHT
=
20/20 VISION

TASTE

Babies have
10,000
tastebuds.

Old people have
5,000
tastebuds.

SMELL

The smell area at the top of the nasal cavity is about the size of your thumbnail.

TOUCH

Our hands have nerve endings under the skin of our fingers that help us feel...

Adult man

Adult woman

HEAT

COLD

PAIN

TOUCH

DRAW YOUR OWN HAND INSIDE THESE TWO OUTLINES. IF YOU HAVE A BABY BROTHER OR SISTER DRAW THEIRS IN TOO!

WATERWORKS

Have you ever thought about how much water you and your family uses every day? You might be surprised to see how much goes down the drain.

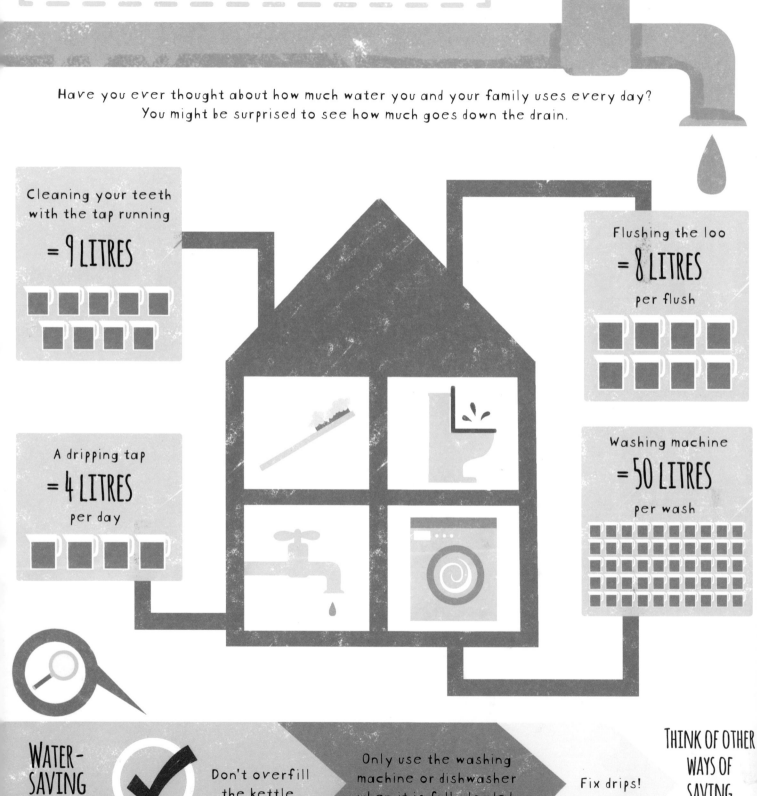

Cleaning your teeth with the tap running

= 9 LITRES

Flushing the loo

= 8 LITRES

per flush

A dripping tap

= 4 LITRES

per day

Washing machine

= 50 LITRES

per wash

WATER-SAVING TIPS

Don't overfill the kettle.

Only use the washing machine or dishwasher when it is fully loaded.

Fix drips!

THINK OF OTHER WAYS OF SAVING WATER.

AMAZING WATER FACTS

Water exists in three different forms (or states) on Earth.

LIQUID

GAS

SOLID

A HUMAN CAN SURVIVE FOR MORE THAN **30 DAYS** WITHOUT FOOD.

BUT LESS THAN **7 DAYS** WITHOUT WATER.

MORE THAN ONE BILLION

people on Earth do not have safe water to drink.

This is the equivalent to every **SIXTH** person not having safe water.

TWO THIRDS OF OUR BODIES ARE MADE OF WATER.

There is the same amount of water on Earth today as there was when the dinosaurs roamed the planet.

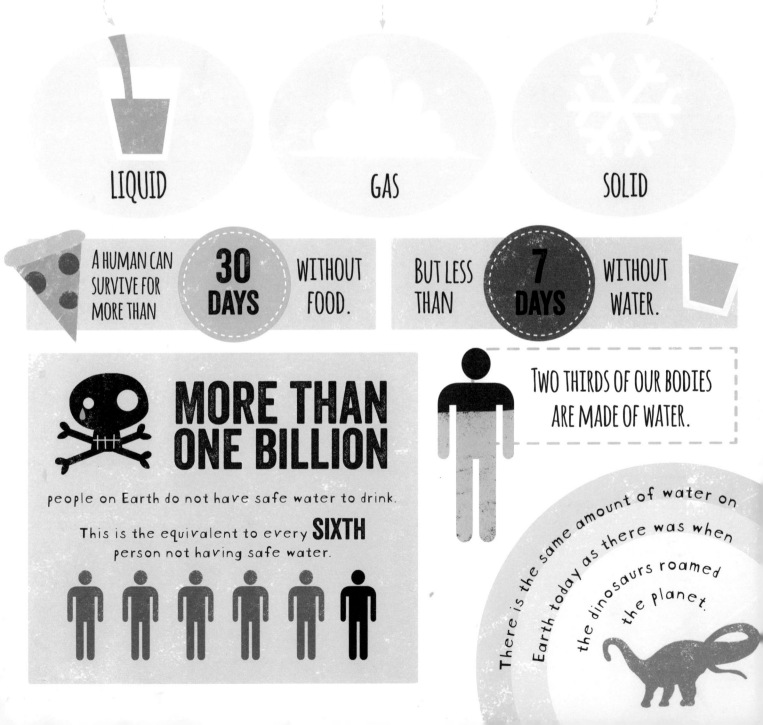

PAWS & POO

The best way to identify animals in the wild is to spot their poo or paw prints. It is much harder to see the animals themselves, but they leave these signs behind for us to track them.

GRIZZLY BEAR

DEER

TIGER

RAT

CAN YOU GUESS WHICH PAW PRINTS AND POO BELONG TO EACH ANIMAL? COMPLETE THE INFOGRAPHIC BY DRAWING IN A TRAIL OF PRINTS TO CONNECT THEM.

Fossilised dinosaur poo is called a coprolite!

A World of Trees

LEAVES NEED SUNLIGHT FOR GROWTH.

Humans breathe

IN oxygen

&

OUT carbon dioxide.

Trees breathe

IN carbon dioxide

&

OUT oxygen.

So, we need trees!

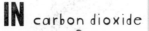

TIMBER FROM TREES IS USED FOR BUILDINGS, DOORS, FLOORS, FURNITURE, FUEL, SHIPS, FENCING, TOOL HANDLES AND PAPER.

SAP GIVES US MAPLE SYRUP AND LATEX (RUBBER).

ROOTS OF THE TREES TAKE IN WATER.

CAN YOU COUNT THE RINGS TO TELL HOW OLD THIS TREE IS?

The science of tree rings is called **DENDROCHRONOLOGY**.

The tallest tree is the giant redwood or sequoia of North America. It can grow higher than 106 metres (350 feet).

The oldest tree in the world is the bristlecone pine. It is as ancient as the Great Pyramid in Egypt – about 5,000 years old.

AMAZING ANIMAL JOURNEYS

Some creatures make the most incredible journeys, or migrations, every year.

Arctic (Start here.)

Antarctic

ARCTIC TERN

Migrates from the Arctic to the Antarctic and back again each year.

THIS ROUTE = 3 TIMES

the distance from the Earth to the Moon in the bird's lifetime.

Canada

USA

Mexico

MONARCH BUTTERFLY

Masses of these North American butterflies migrate from north to south for the winter (and back again in spring). One route is over

3,200 KILOMETRES (ALMOST 2,000 MILES) LONG.

→ autumn migration

→ spring migration

Grey Whale

Migrates from feeding grounds in the Arctic to Mexico

= 8,000 KILOMETRES (5,000 MILES).

Baby whales are born and then make the return trip up north with their mothers.

Total trip for adult whale
= 16,000 KILOMETRES (10,000 MILES).

N
W E
S

Alaska (USA)

Canada

USA

Mexico

THINK OF THE LONGEST JOURNEY YOU HAVE EVER BEEN ON.
SEE IF YOU CAN DRAW IT ON THIS MAP OF THE WORLD.

YOU COULD ALSO DRAW
A JOURNEY YOU WOULD
LIKE TO MAKE, USING
A DIFFERENT COLOUR.

WORLD POPULATION TIMELINE GAME

There are 7 billion people in the world today. Let's look at how the world population has grown from the early 1800s to today. You can play this timeline as a board game. You just need some counters and a die.

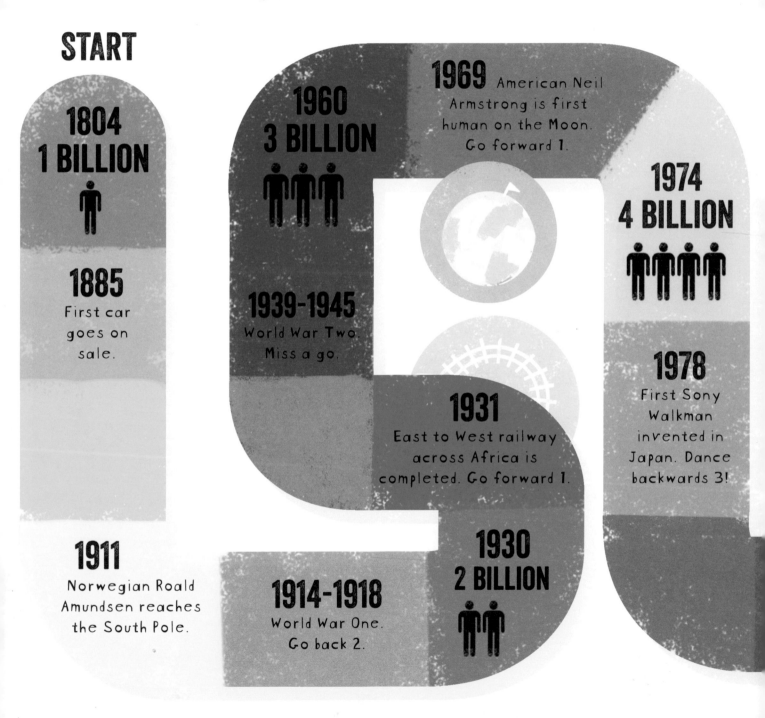

START

1804 1 BILLION

1885 First car goes on sale.

1911 Norwegian Roald Amundsen reaches the South Pole.

1914-1918 World War One. Go back 2.

1930 2 BILLION

1931 East to West railway across Africa is completed. Go forward 1.

1939-1945 World War Two. Miss a go.

1960 3 BILLION

1969 American Neil Armstrong is first human on the Moon. Go forward 1.

1974 4 BILLION

1978 First Sony Walkman invented in Japan. Dance backwards 3!

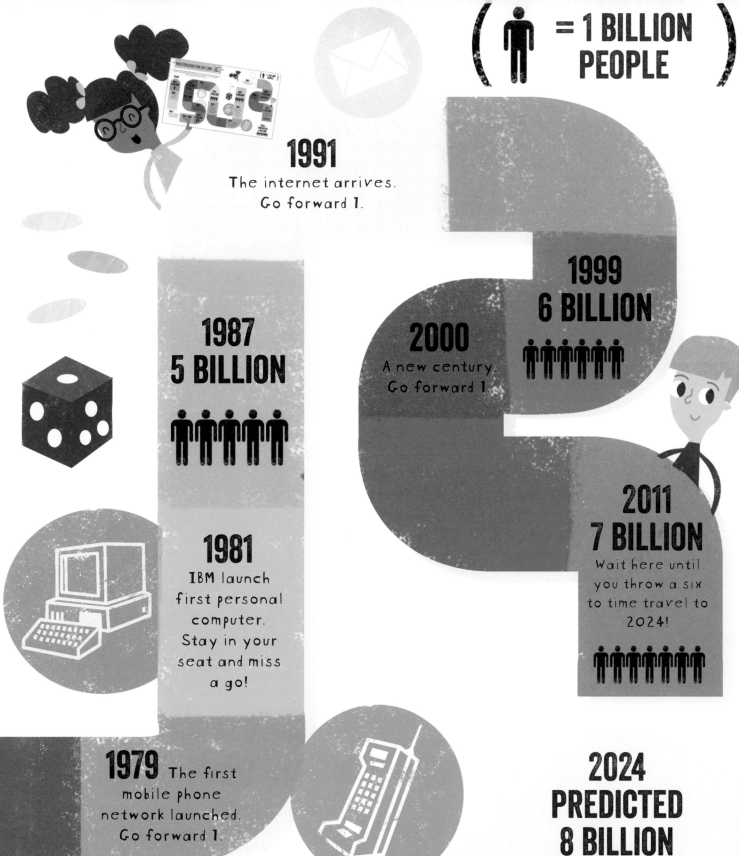

(🚹 = 1 BILLION PEOPLE)

1991
The internet arrives.
Go forward 1.

1987
5 BILLION
🚹🚹🚹🚹🚹

2000
A new century.
Go forward 1

1999
6 BILLION
🚹🚹🚹🚹🚹🚹

1981
IBM launch
first personal
computer.
Stay in your
seat and miss
a go!

2011
7 BILLION
Wait here until
you throw a six
to time travel to
2024!
🚹🚹🚹🚹🚹🚹🚹

1979 The first
mobile phone
network launched.
Go forward 1.

2024
PREDICTED
8 BILLION
🚹🚹🚹🚹🚹🚹🚹🚹

SPIDER WORLD

SPIDERS might frighten some people but they are truly fascinating creatures with some amazing abilities.

Spiders have 6 glands that produce a liquid that turns into silk when it comes into contact with the air.

The spider holds the silk thread with one leg while it creates its web.

1
First the spider makes a large, thread square.

2
Then it makes rays of threads from the middle to the edge.

3
Next it makes spirals from the centre outwards.

4
Finally the spider spins a thread from the centre to a hiding place nearby.

Webs can be up to
3 METRES (9.8 FEET)
across or as small as
a postage stamp.

Spiders are arachnids

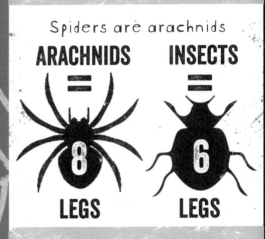

ARACHNIDS = **8** **LEGS**

INSECTS = **6** **LEGS**

Spider silk is
5 TIMES
stronger than steel
of the same diameter.

There are around
40,000
different species of spider.

Spiders are found on every
continent of the world apart
from Antarctica.

THERE'S NO SPIDER
ON THIS WEB.
CAN YOU DRAW ONE ON?

ANIMAL SUPERHEROES

Plants and animals have features that suit where they live and how they find food. Let's take a closer look at some unusual ones and their special adaptations.

PUFFINS

Puffins may look like clowns but they are really well adapted for their hard life in the cold Atlantic Ocean.

POWERFUL WINGS

for flying in the air and also diving to **24 METRES (80 FEET).**

Bills laced with **SHARP HOOKS** to catch lots of fish in one go.

WEBBED FEET

used for steering under water.

SPECIAL OIL GLAND

by tail to keep feathers waterproof.

FIND OUT ABOUT SOME OTHER ANIMALS.
HOW DO THEY PROTECT THEMSELVES OR HUNT FOR FOOD?
HOW HAVE THEY ADAPTED TO SUIT WHERE THEY LIVE?

FLEXIBLE ARMOUR so it can curl into a ball that no other animal can break into.

PANGOLIN

It looks like a living pinecone!

CLAWS
that can dig through ground as hard as concrete to get at food.

SUPER SENSE OF SMELL
to find ants and termites to eat from hundreds of metres away.

BIG EYES
to help it see in the dark.

AYE-AYE

Nocturnal with enormous orange eyes.

BUSHY TAIL
to help balance in trees.

EXTRA LONG MIDDLE FINGER
to pry insects and grubs out of tree trunks.

CONTINENTAL DRIFT

The land on **EARTH** is divided into **SEVEN CONTINENTS.** All the continents were once joined in one huge supercontinent called **PANGAEA** The continents are still moving a few centimetres a year.

The **THREE** largest countries in **NORTH AMERICA** are Canada, the United States of America and Mexico.

Over **1,300** languages are spoken in **AFRICA.**

Brazil is the largest country in **SOUTH AMERICA.** The national language of Brazil is Portuguese.

There are no native people in **ANTARCTICA.** There are only scientists from many different countries.

ASIA

is the biggest continent. Europe and Africa would both fit into it with a bit of room left over. India is so big it is called a subcontinent.

EUROPE

is the smallest continent, but it has about

225

native languages.

OCEANIA

is counted as a continent. It is made up of Australia, New Zealand and other islands in the Pacific Ocean. There are

14 OFFICIAL

languages spoken.

FIND YOUR OWN CONTINENT AND WRITE IN WHERE YOU LIVE AND THE LANGUAGE OR LANGUAGES YOU SPEAK.

PHARAOH'S MUMMY

The Ancient Egyptians believed in life after death so it was very important that their bodies were carefully prepared and preserved.

PEPPERCORNS
used to keep shape of nose.

FALSE EYES, SOMETIMES ONIONS,
used to keep eyeball shapes.

BODY COATED WITH OILS.

BODY DRIED FOR
40 DAYS

1 **MUMMIFICATION TOOK** → **70 DAYS**

2 **WRAPPED IN MANY LAYERS**
of linen bandages with amulets for protection.

The Ancient Egyptians invented one of the very first languages to be written down. It was called hieroglyphics and made up of beautiful pictures of birds and animals. There are over **700** glyphs.

CAN YOU FIND OUT SOME MORE ABOUT THEM AND EVEN TRY DRAWING SOME?

3 Cover of **PAINTED WOOD** placed on top.

4 First coffin **COVERED IN GOLD.** Gold was a symbol of the sun god Ra.

5 Second coffin was **BEAUTIFULLY DECORATED.** (With a portrait of the person.)

BIKE RACE THROUGH TIME

BICYCLES HAVE BEEN AROUND FOR NEARLY 200 YEARS NOW.
THEY'VE CERTAINLY CHANGED A LOT THROUGH THE AGES.

1817
Dandy Horse invented in Germany. No pedals and the rider had to push it along using their feet.

1839
Pedals put on a Dandy Horse. First real bike had been made.

1920s
Bikes for kids became popular.

1960s
Racing bikes developed with dropped handlebars, narrow tyres and lots of gears.

1899
Three-speed gears invented.

1970s
Chopper bikes, based on the look of motorbikes. BMX (Bicycle Motorcross) for dirt-track racing and stunts.

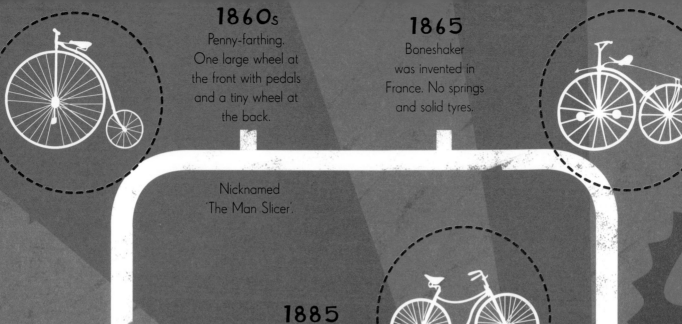

1860s
Penny-farthing. One large wheel at the front with pedals and a tiny wheel at the back.

1865
Boneshaker was invented in France. No springs and solid tyres.

Nicknamed 'The Man Slicer'.

1885
'Safety' bicycle with smaller wheels of same size and a chain.

1888
Tyres with air in them (pneumatic tyres) replaced solid tyres.

1980s
Mountain bikes with strong frames and flat handlebars.

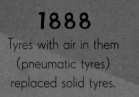

DRAW YOUR OWN BIKE OR MAYBE ONE YOU WOULD LIKE TO INVENT!

ANIMAL ATHLETES

Can an ant be stronger than a human? You might be surprised by how much some creatures can lift, or how high they can jump compared to us.

LEAF-CUTTER ANT

can carry a piece of leaf

50 TIMES

its own body weight.

Like a human lifting a
MEDIUM-SIZED VAN.

MALE RHINOCEROS BEETLE

can lift

850 TIMES

its body weight.

Like a human lifting

8 DOUBLE-DECKER BUSES!

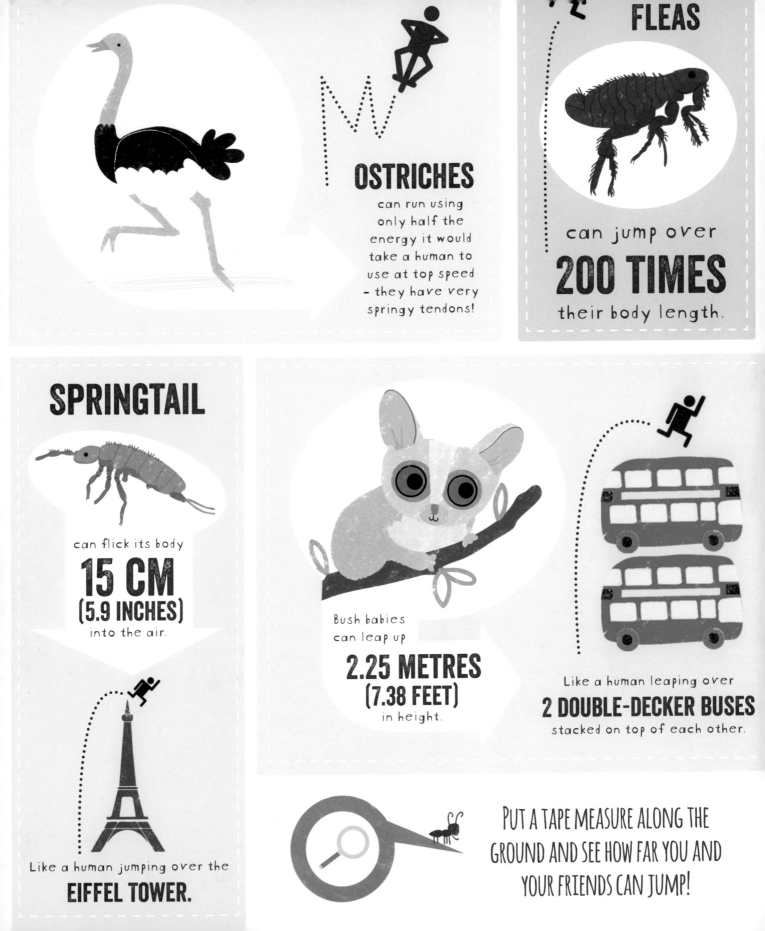

OSTRICHES

can run using only half the energy it would take a human to use at top speed – they have very springy tendons!

FLEAS

can jump over **200 TIMES** their body length.

SPRINGTAIL

can flick its body **15 CM (5.9 INCHES)** into the air.

Like a human jumping over the **EIFFEL TOWER.**

Bush babies can leap up **2.25 METRES (7.38 FEET)** in height.

Like a human leaping over **2 DOUBLE-DECKER BUSES** stacked on top of each other.

PUT A TAPE MEASURE ALONG THE GROUND AND SEE HOW FAR YOU AND YOUR FRIENDS CAN JUMP!

HOW DEEP AND HIGH?

Sometimes it's hard to imagine just how deep or how high something is. It can be helpful to compare it to something we might have seen like the Eiffel Tower in Paris, France.

Eiffel Tower
=
324
metres high
(1063 feet)

162 tall men of 2 metres (6.5 feet) in height would fit into it.

1/3

3

Nearly **5**

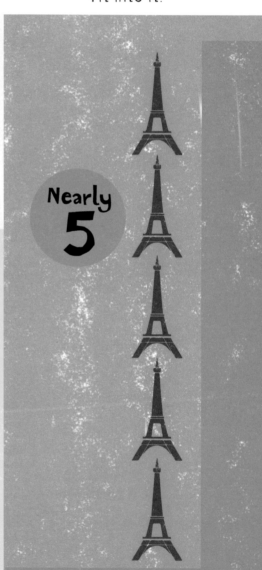

Tallest trees in the world - the giant redwoods.

Angel Falls in Venezuela - 979 metres (3,212 feet) high.

Grand Canyon in the United States of America is 1.6 kilometres (nearly 1 mile) deep in places.

5

27

34

CAN YOU FIND OUT
HOW FAR IT IS FROM
THE EARTH TO THE
MOON?
HOW LONG DOES
IT TAKE TO GET
THERE?

Lake Baikal in Russia -
nearly 1,700 metres
(5,577 feet) deep at its
deepest point.

Mount Everest on the
border of Nepal and
Tibet is 8,848 metres
(29,029 feet) high.

The Mariana Trench in
the Pacific Ocean is
11,034 metres
(36,201 feet) deep.

From Earth to
the Moon.

ALIEN'S GUIDE TO PLANET EARTH

IMAGINE AN ALIEN IS VISITING OUR PLANET. WHAT DO THEY NEED TO KNOW ABOUT IT?

MERCURY

VENUS

MARS

EARTH IS

THE **THIRD** PLANET FROM THE SUN.

THE **5TH** LARGEST PLANET IN THE SOLAR SYSTEM.

EARTH **ORBITS** THE SUN ONCE EVERY **365¼** DAYS.

ONE EARTH YEAR =

365¼ DAYS

WE SAVE THE ¼s UP

¼ + ¼ + ¼ + ¼

= 1 EXTRA DAY EVERY 4 YEARS

= **LEAP YEAR** (366 DAYS).

EXTRA DAY IS ALWAYS **29TH FEBRUARY.**

EARTH HAS **ONE MOON**

MOON ORBITS THE EARTH **ONCE** EVERY **28 DAYS** --> = 1 EARTH MONTH

EARTH IS NEARLY **50** TIMES BIGGER THAN THE MOON.

JUPITER SATURN URANUS NEPTUNE PLUTO

Pluto used to be the ninth PLANET but in 2006 some scientists decided it should be called a DWARF PLANET. However, not all scientists agree with this.

DAY AND NIGHT

EARTH SPINS ONCE ON ITS OWN AXIS EVERY 24 HOURS

DAYTIME   NIGHT-TIME

AIR ON EARTH
INCLUDES DIFFERENT GASES:

NITROGEN 78%

OXYGEN 21%
The humans who live on Earth breathe this to stay alive!

other gases including
ARGON AND CARBON DIOXIDE

PLANET EARTH IS ALSO CALLED **'THE BLUE PLANET'.** WATER COVERS ABOUT **TWO THIRDS** OF IT.

29% LAND

71% WATER

CAN YOU FIND OUT SOME OTHER FASCINATING EARTH FACTS ABOUT OUR BEAUTIFUL PLANET FOR OUR ALIEN VISITORS?

MUGSHOTS

People have always liked pictures of themselves. Since early times portraits have been made in all sorts of styles.

ANCIENT EGYPTIAN WALL PAINTINGS OF PHARAOHS

* Head always a side view.

* Eye is a front view.

* Shoulders and chest as seen from the front.

* Rest of body drawn as a side view.

* Very long feet.

COURT PAINTINGS OF ROYALTY

to show how powerful and rich they were.

ANCIENT GREEK BUSTS

followed a rule called **THE GOLDEN MEAN.**

The tip of the nose is halfway between the eyes and chin.

The mouth is halfway between the nose and the chin.

CHINESE SCROLL PAINTINGS

on paper or silk.

VICTORIAN PHOTOGRAPHS - DON'T say cheese!

PASSPORT PHOTOS FROM A BOOTH!

MINIATURES for loved ones to carry with them.

DIGITAL PHOTOS AND SELFIES ON MOBILES to send to your friends and family.

SELF-PORTRAIT

DRAW, PAINT OR TAKE A PHOTOGRAPH OF YOURSELF, OR A FRIEND, TO FIT WITHIN THE FRAME.

CLOUD-SPOTTING

Clouds are made from tiny drops of water or ice crystals.
Different types of clouds form at different heights in the sky.

CIRROSTRATUS - thin sheet. Often causes a halo effect around the sun or moon.

ALTOSTRATUS - smooth white or grey sheet across the sky. Sun might just be visible in a watery way. Sign of rain.

CUMULUS - heavy, cauliflower-shaped clouds with flat bases. Heaped-up piles. Can change into...

CUMULONIMBUS - may reach great heights and spread out at the top in the shape of an anvil. Causes heavy rain, lightning and thunder. Sometimes even tornadoes.

CIRRUS - always made of ice. Looks like wisps of hair or feather. Long trails.

ALTOCUMULUS - layers of blob-shaped clouds in groups or lines.

CIRROCUMULUS - looks like ripples in the sand on the seashore or like the pattern on the back of a mackerel. Can mean rain is on the way, especially if other cirrus or cirrostratus clouds are around.

STRATOCUMULUS - not as even in thickness as stratus. Light and dark areas on the bottom show that there are piles of clouds in the layer.

NIMBOSTRATUS - hanging low, dark, grey and threatening. Brings heavy rain or snow.

STRATUS - low, smooth, even sheet. Often blots out high ground. May turn to fog, drizzle or rain.

WEIRD WEATHER

If all the ice in the Antarctic melted the oceans would rise up by **67 METRES (220 FEET)**. This is as high as a **20-STOREY** building.

If you put 10 cm (4 inches) of snow into a glass it would produce 1 cm (0.4 inches) of water!

10 CM ～～ 1 CM

So much snow fell one year at Mount Baker in the USA that it was enough to bury a house completely.

The driest place on Earth is Arica, Chile in South America. It would take

100 YEARS

to fill up a cup with rainwater!

SNOWFLAKES CAN TAKE UP TO AN HOUR TO FALL TO THE GROUND.

ASTRAPHOBIA
is the fear of

THUNDER and LIGHTNING.

In Mawsynram in India they have so much rain that a year's worth would cover two double-decker buses.

THERE ARE ABOUT **16 MILLION** LIGHTNING STORMS AROUND THE WORLD EVERY YEAR WITH ABOUT **100 LIGHTNING** FLASHES HAPPENING **EVERY SECOND**.

Largest hailstone ever recorded was in Nebraska, USA in 2003. It was **17.8 CM (7 INCHES)** in diameter. This is as big as a bowling ball!